Follow Me

Story by Neil Griffiths

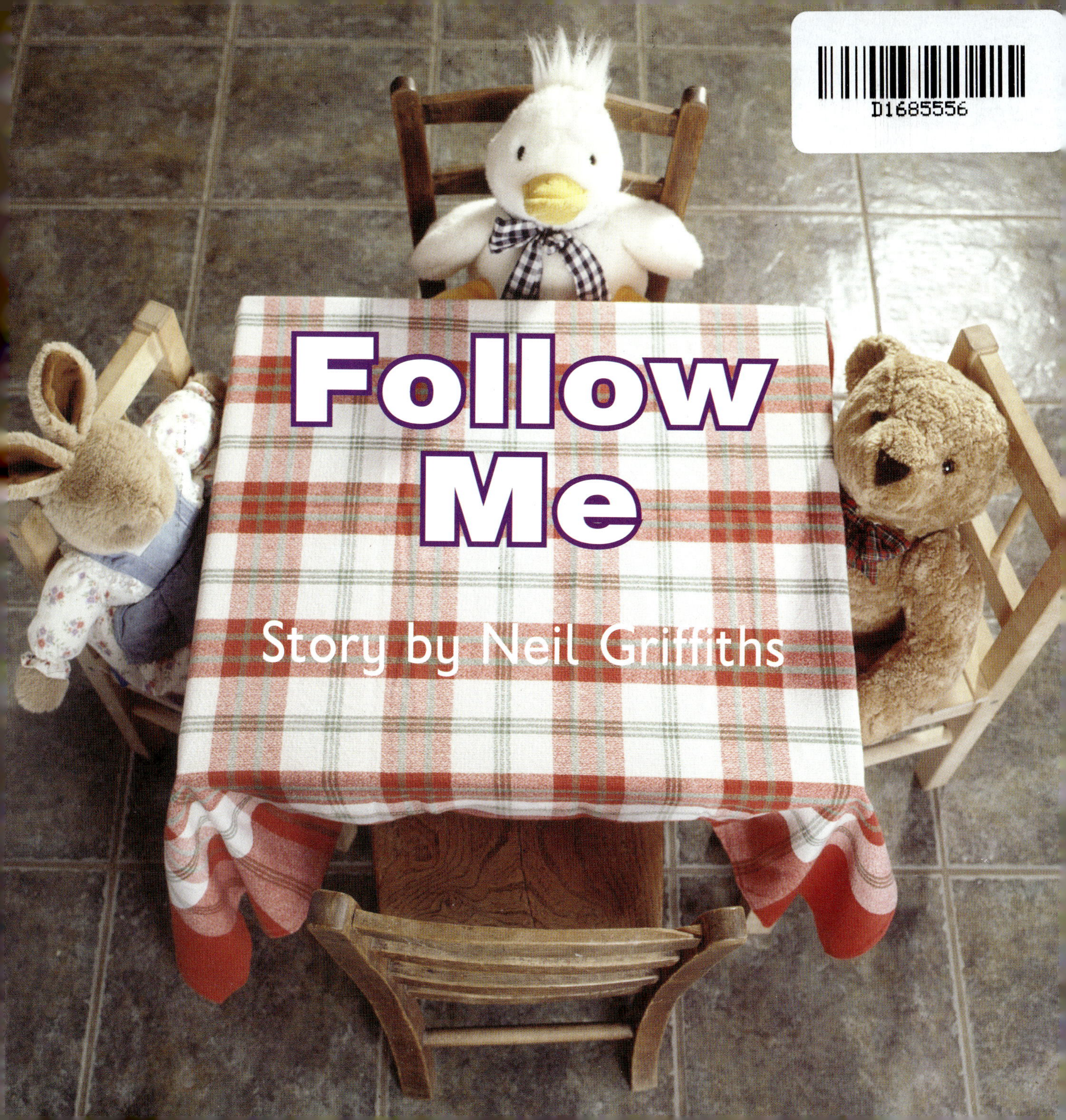

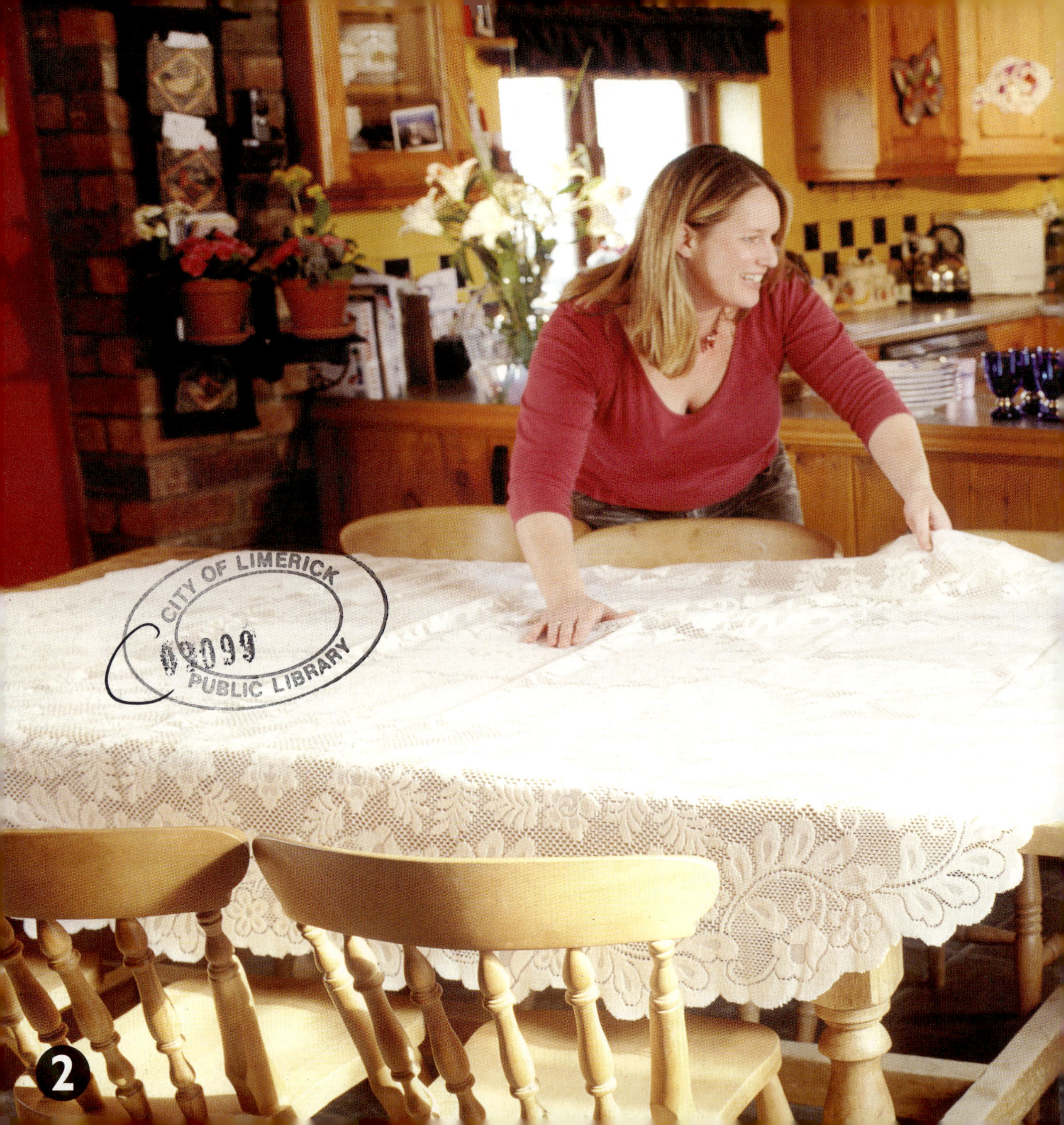
2

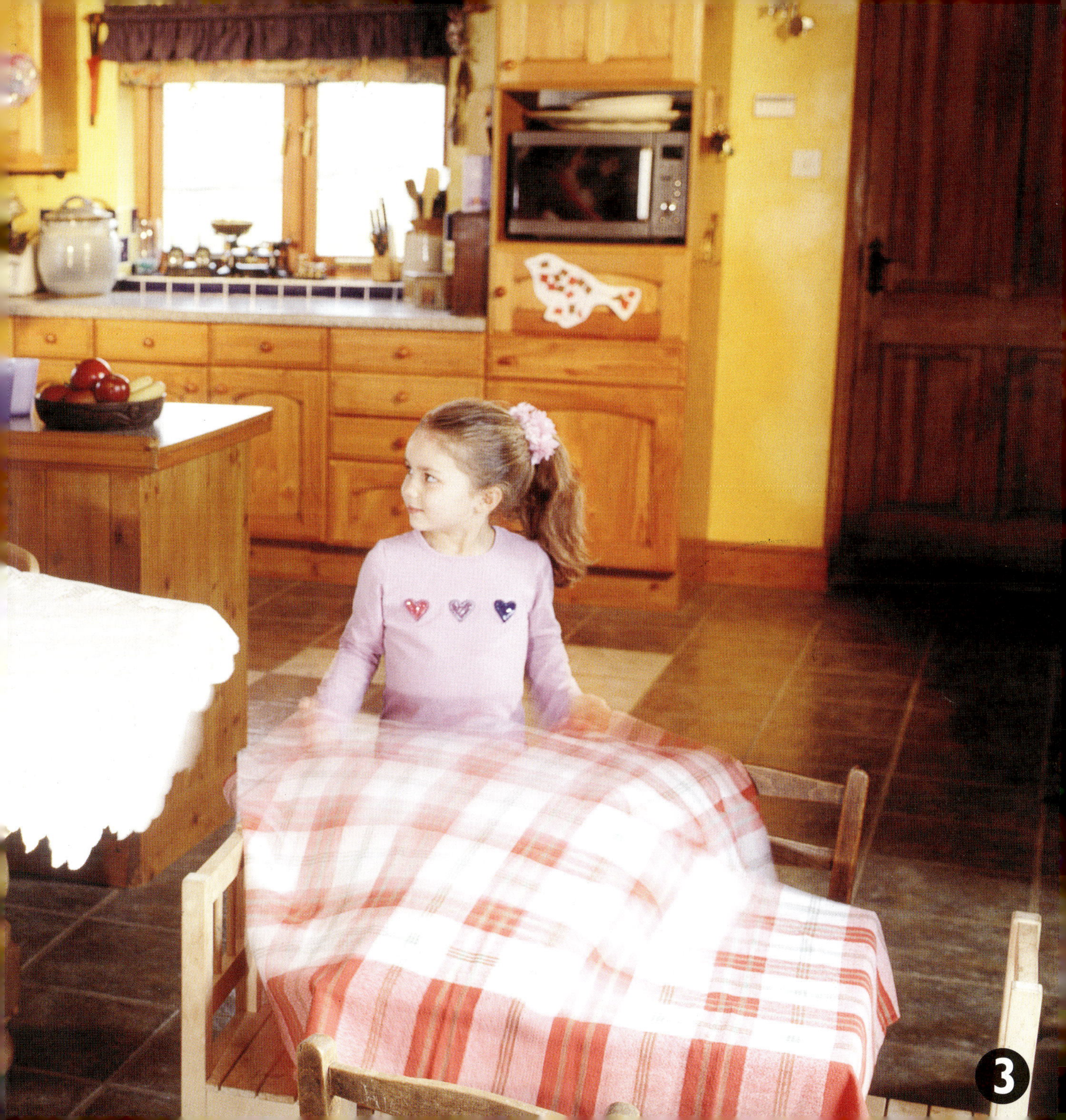

3

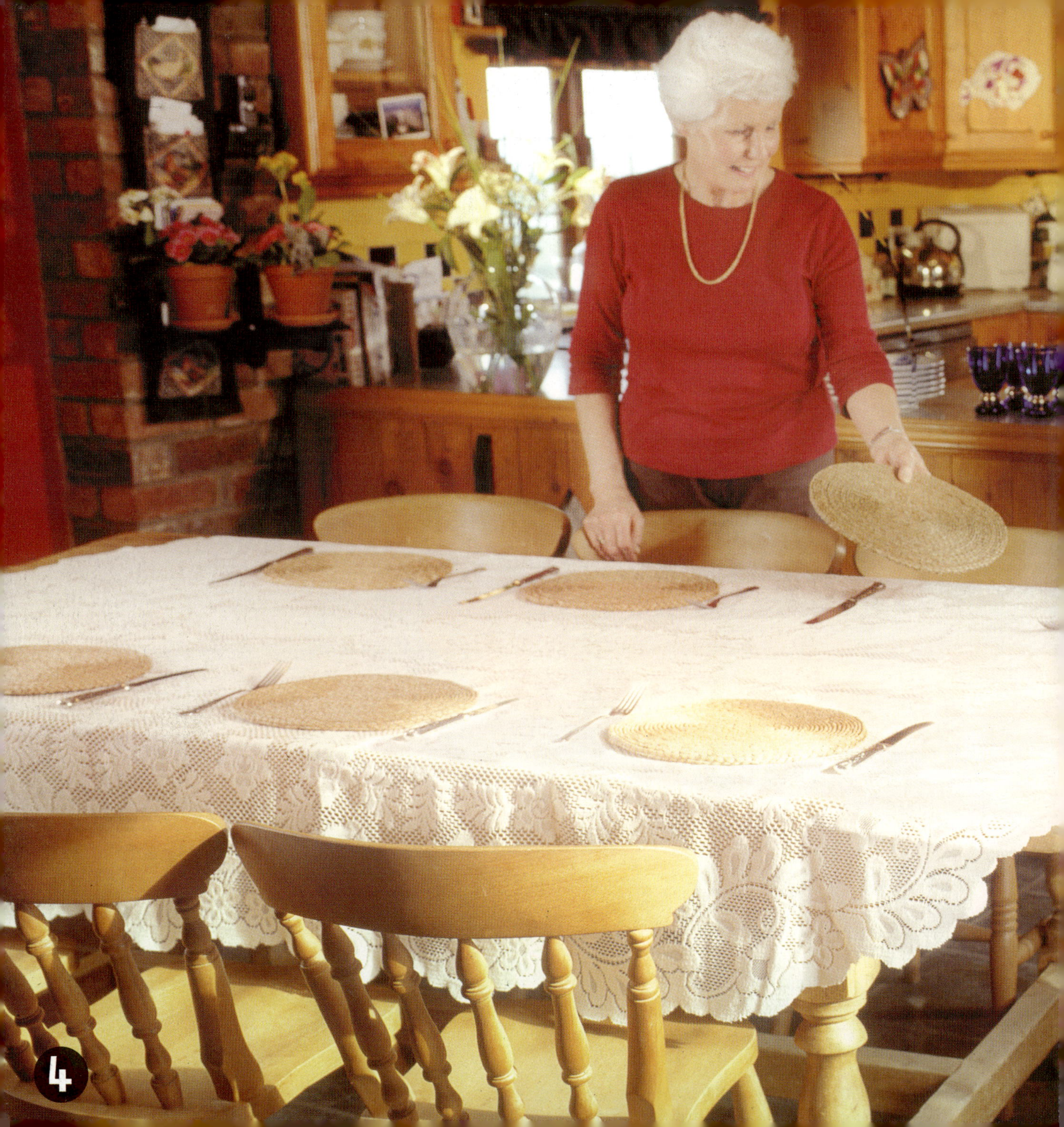
4

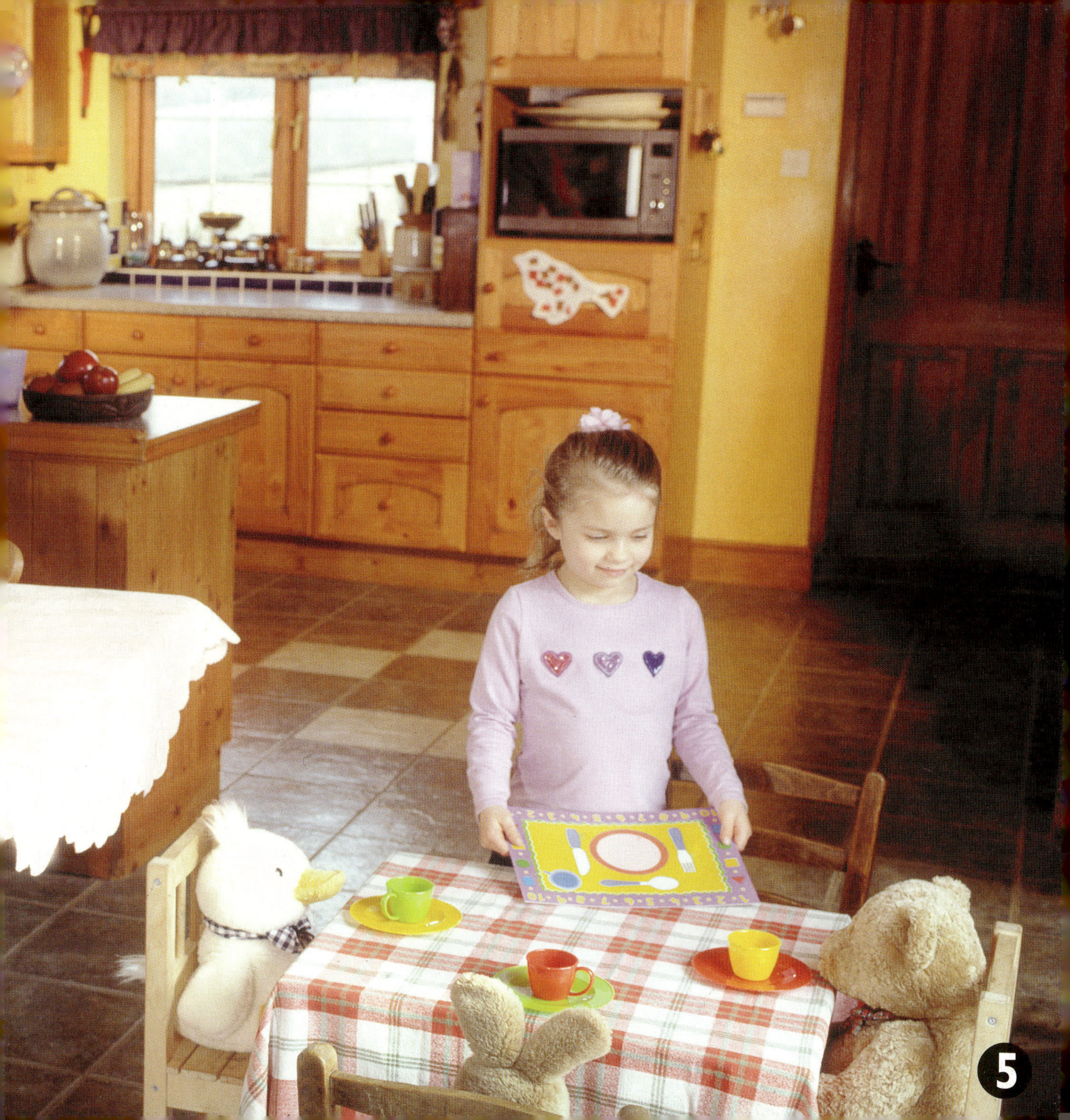

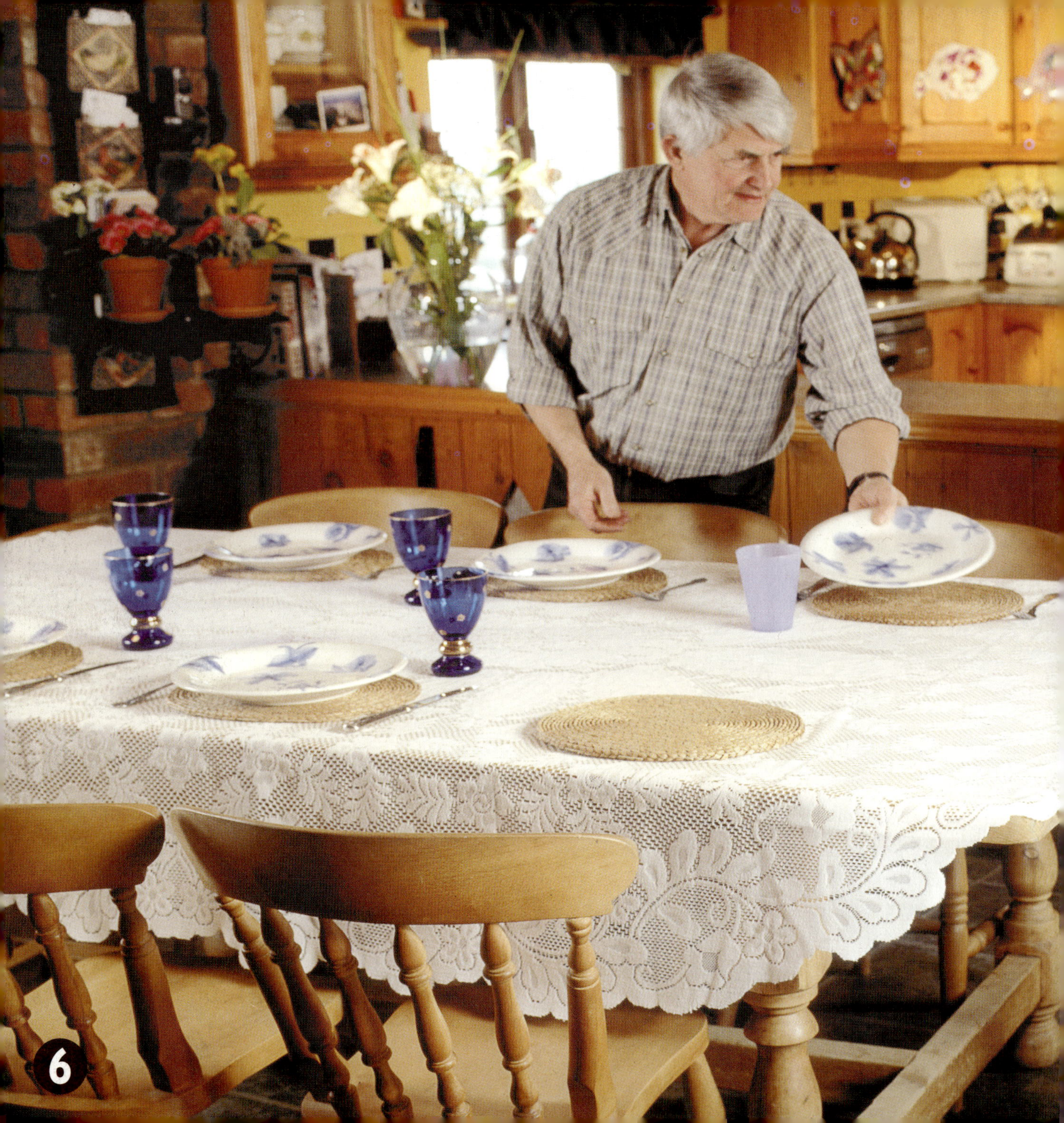
6

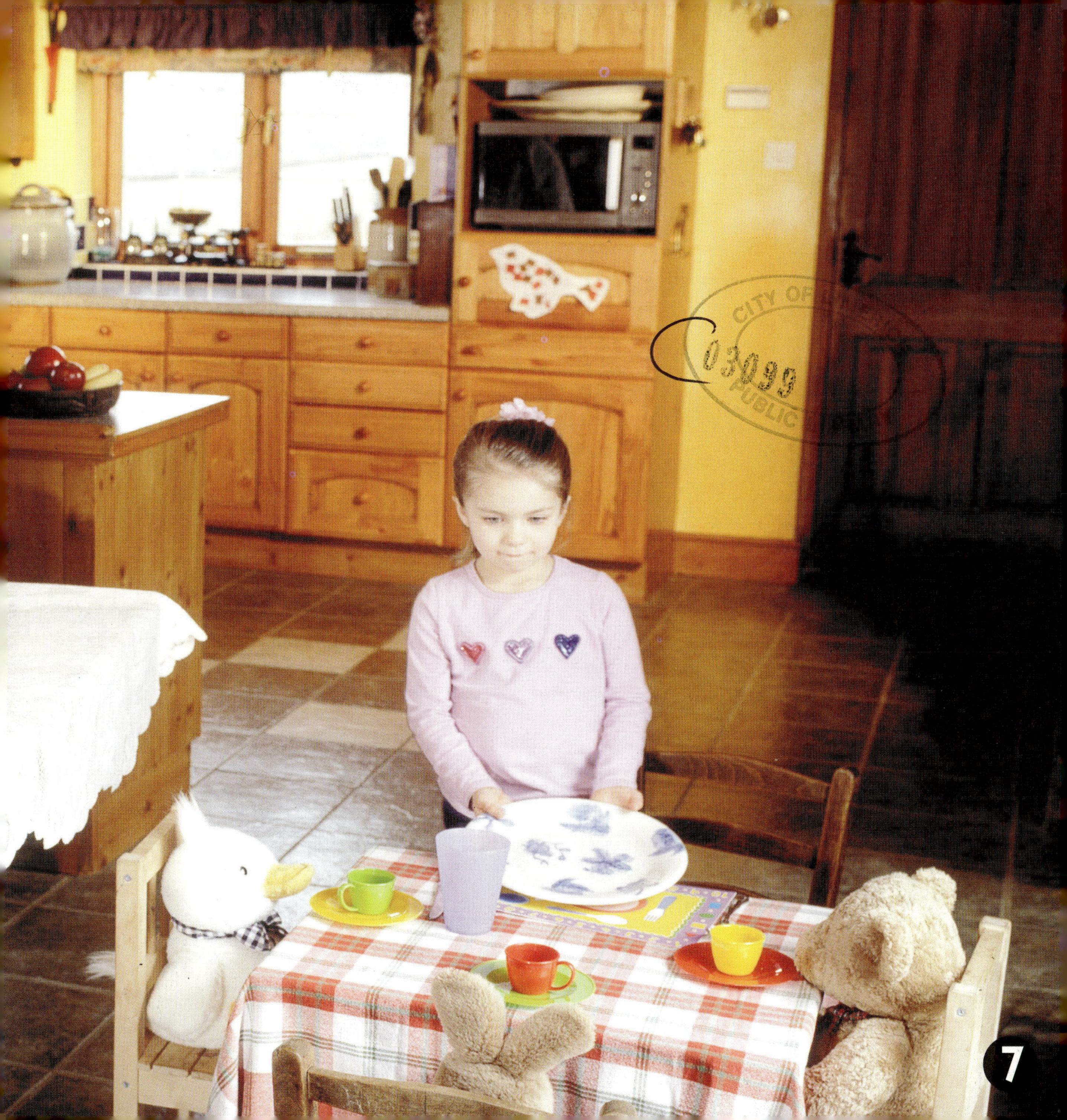

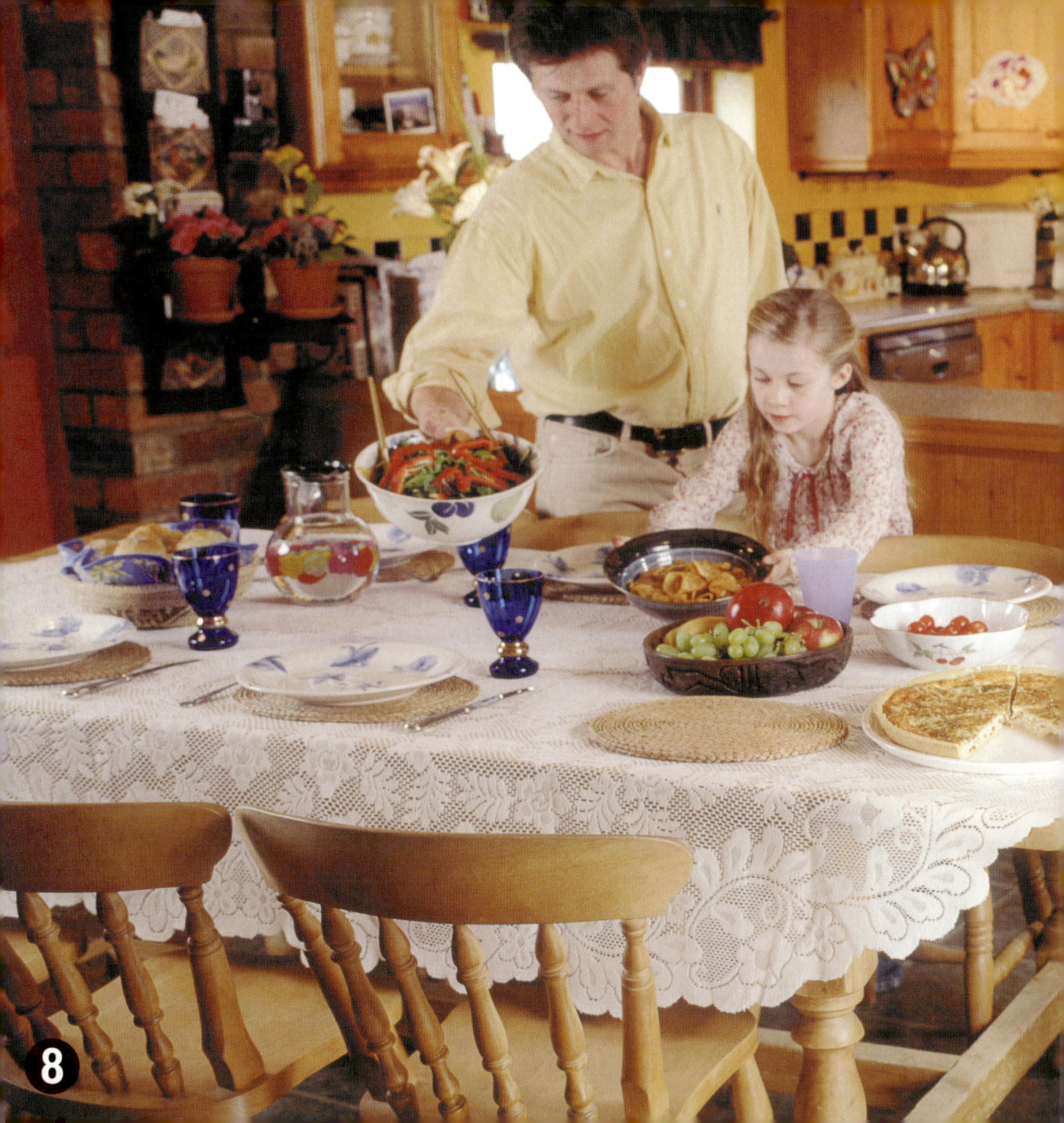

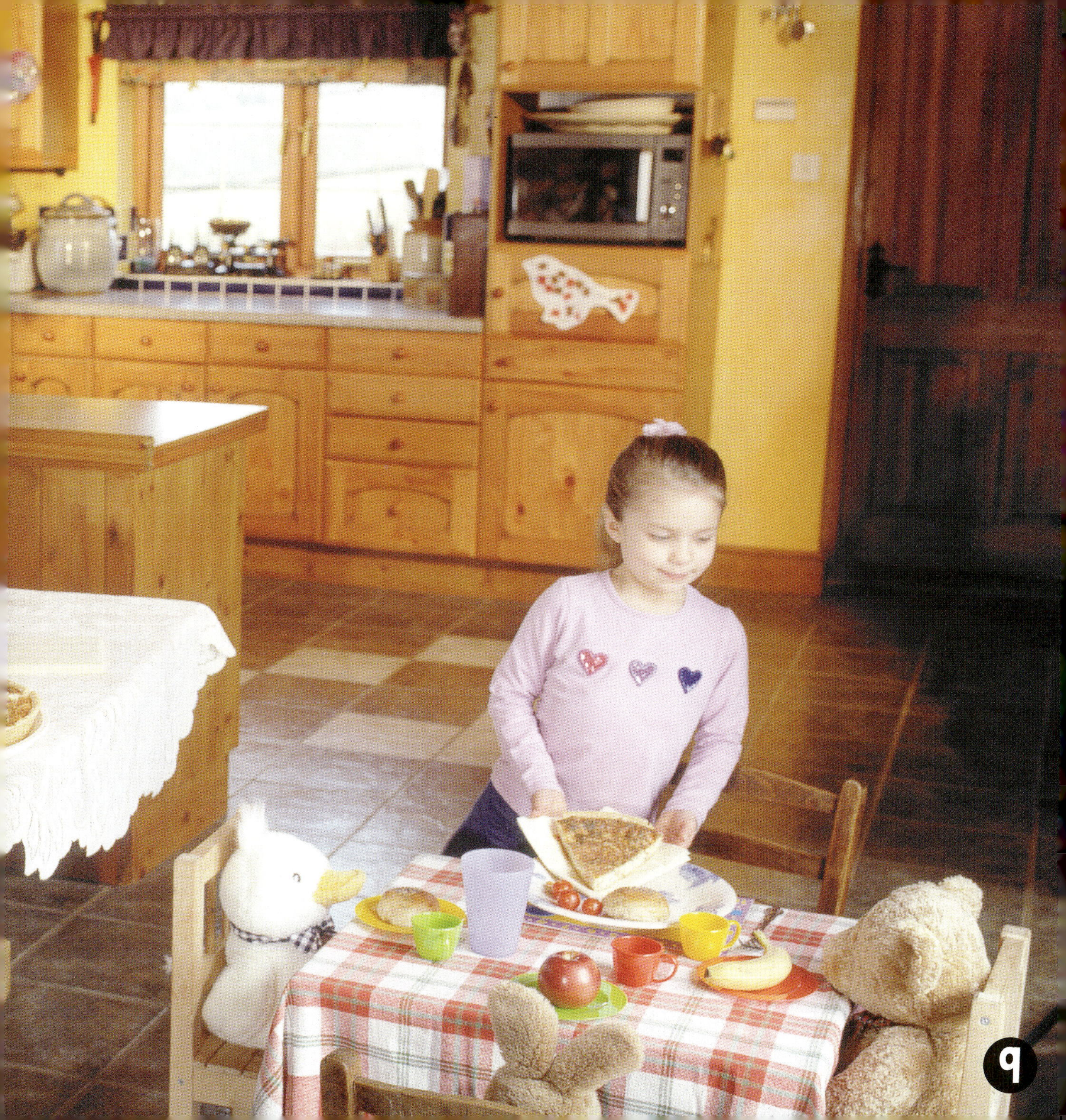

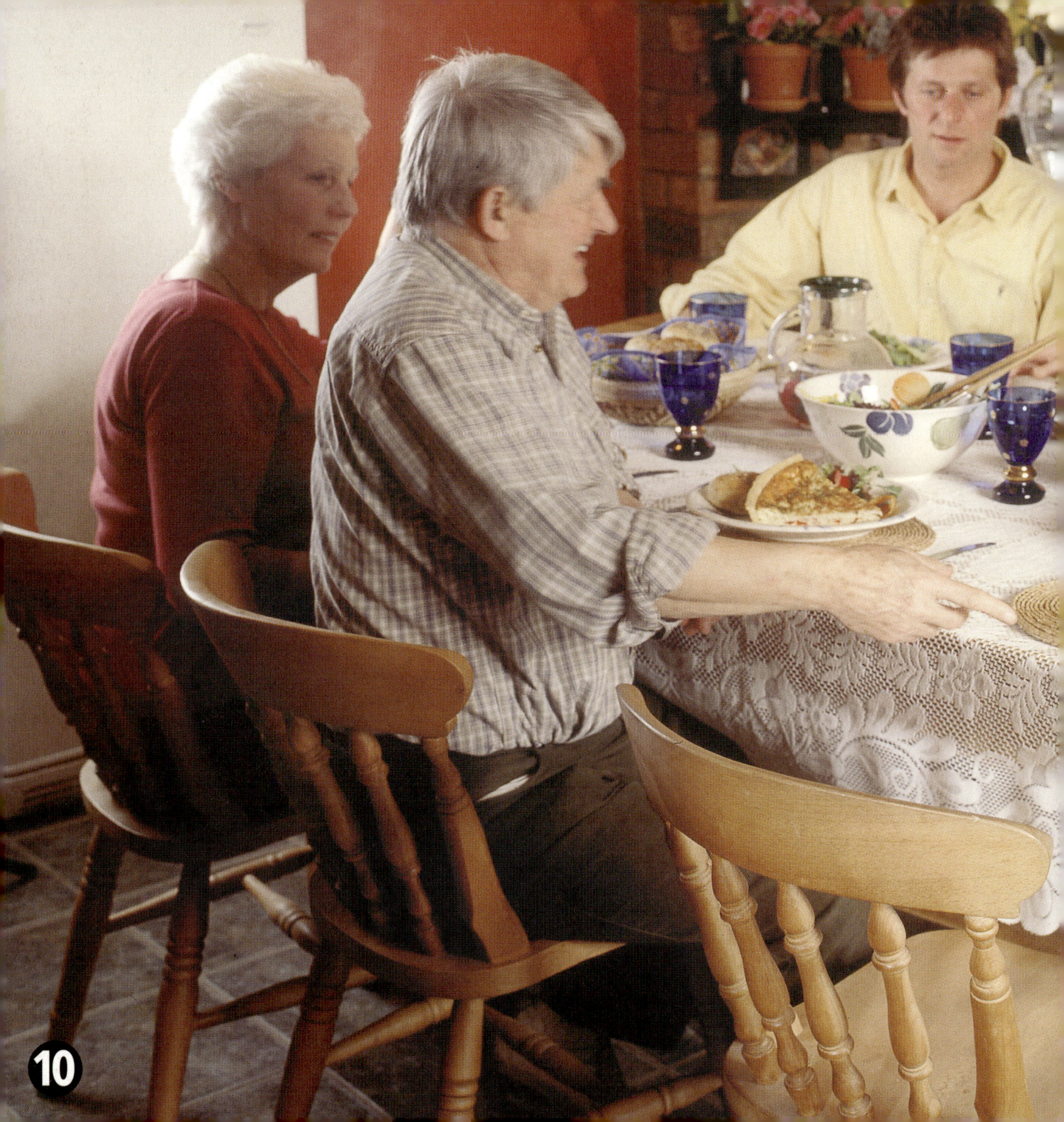

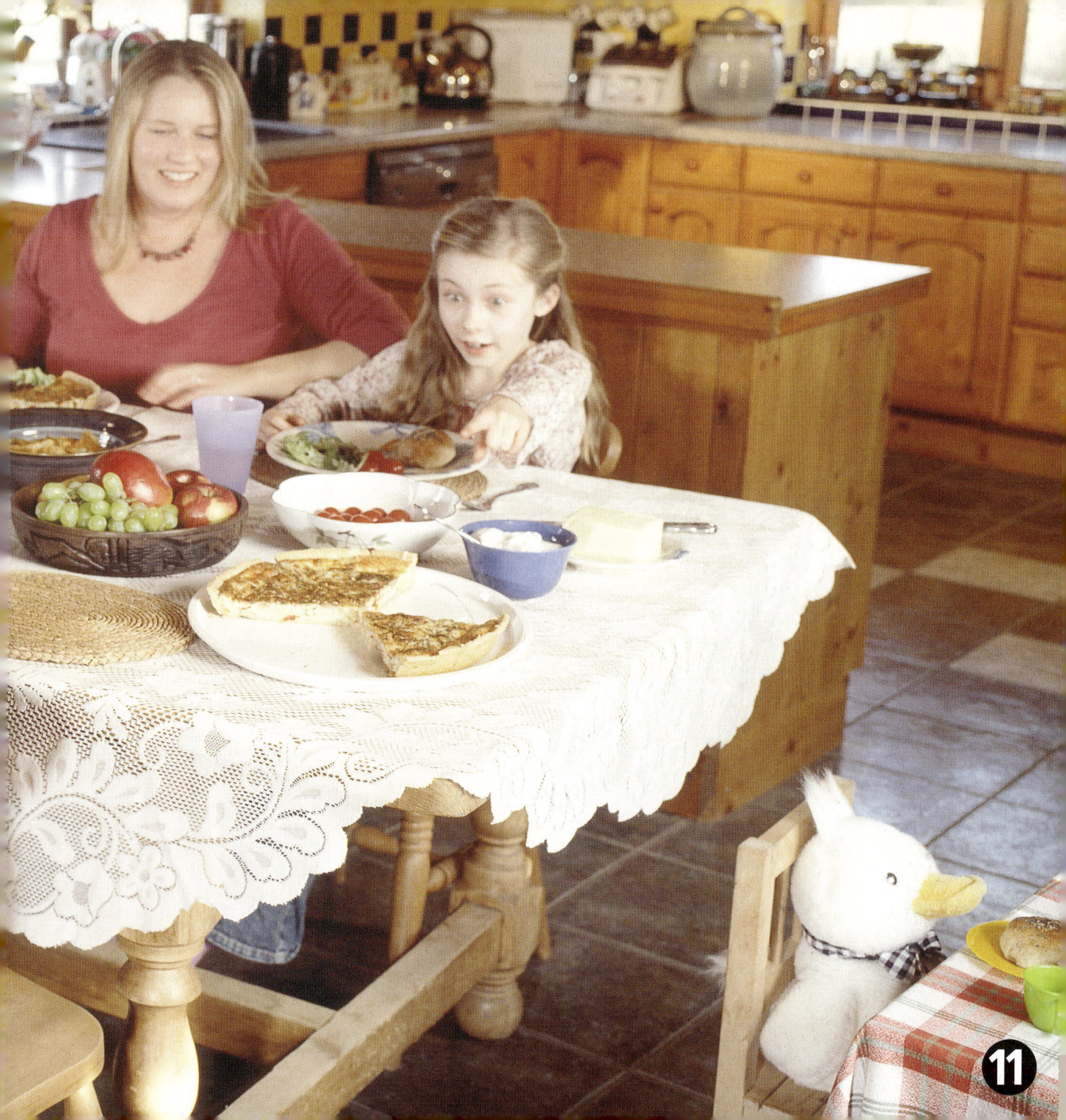

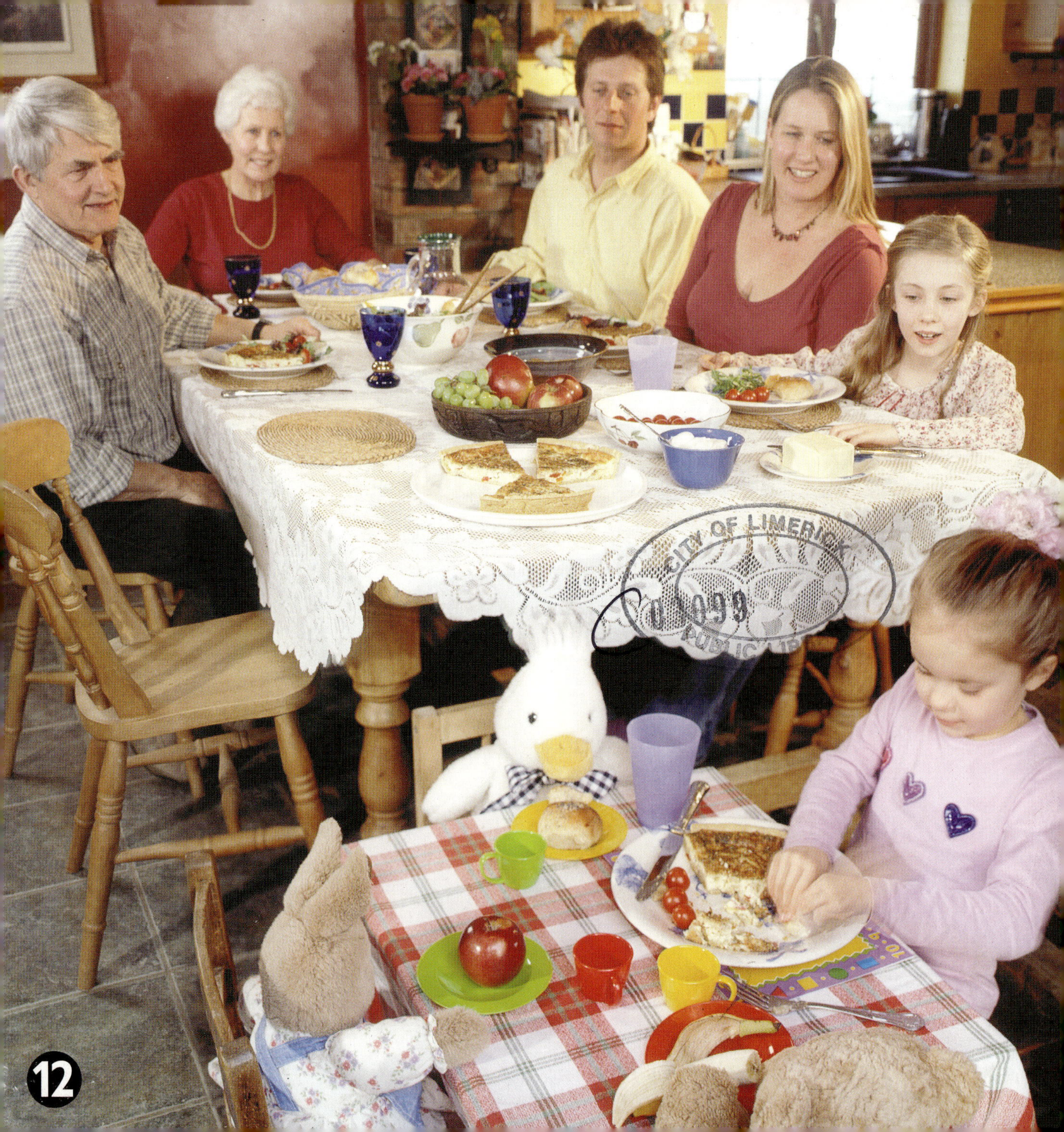